The Grass Pipe

The Grass Pipe

by Robert Coles

An Atlantic Monthly Press Book

Little, Brown and Company   BOSTON   TORONTO

LIBRARY OF CONGRESS CATALOG CARD NO. 69–15758

Second Printing

ATLANTIC–LITTLE, BROWN BOOKS
ARE PUBLISHED BY
LITTLE, BROWN AND COMPANY
IN ASSOCIATION WITH
THE ATLANTIC MONTHLY PRESS

Published simultaneously in Canada
by Little, Brown & Company (Canada) Limited

PRINTED IN THE UNITED STATES OF AMERICA

To My Mother and Father

The Grass Pipe

No, I can't say why I took pot. I don't think I'm much different from any other ninth grader. I never used to talk about "trips" or "pot" or "grass." I knew there was something called marijuana, but I knew it like you know the capital of France is Paris. I didn't think about it. Now I know how to take it.

To me "drugs" used to mean something that made you healthy by changing the way the body works or by killing a germ. I never connected the word with LSD or pot, not when I first heard about them. My father takes drugs, to calm himself down and for his ulcer. I thought pot might be something like the drugs he uses for his "nerves" — you know, something that gets to you and makes you feel good. It sounds strange and mysterious, all the talk about pot and LSD and addicts. When I heard that kids like Charlie and Tom and me were called "dope addicts" by some people, I was mad. We're not dope addicts. That's crazy talk.

Charlie and Tom are part of the picture. I'm not blaming anyone, but if it hadn't been for them, especially Charlie, I don't think I would have tried pot. The three of us are old friends — "Paul, Charlie, and Tom, the three," my dad used to call us. My dad is a lawyer, a partner in a big law firm. He used to joke with us and tell us that maybe someday we would be lawyers and be in the same firm. We'd make a lot of money together.

We became friends almost by accident. We were the three tallest guys in the class in the fourth grade. We didn't live on the same street, just nearby. But the teacher put us in the back of the room and kept on reminding us how tall we were and how we would block the other kids' vision if we didn't sit in back — and how we should be *examples* to them. Over and over she said we were taller, so we should be more grown-up. We should keep quiet and be good examples. Well, we liked the attention, but we weren't always that good.

It didn't take long for people to start calling us the Three Musketeers, and we got kicks out of that. Even the teacher joined in — I can hear her, Miss Herlihy, saying, "If the Three Musketeers will kindly stop whispering, the class can go ahead with its next assignment." Everyone would whirl around, and Charlie and Tom and I would look at each other and then stare straight ahead — but we'd be fighting not to smile.

She really did depend on us, Miss Herlihy. One day she had us stay late and told us how "responsible" we must be, how children need to follow "leaders," and how we were big strong boys, and we were the "natural leaders" of the class. I went home and told my parents that, and they said "Great," but I knew they weren't impressed.

The three of us took turns being head monitor of the class, but the main thing was that we became real good friends. Charlie and Tom were the first friends I ever had away from my own street, and we stuck together. Even though we got separated the next year, in the fifth grade, and never were together again in a class, outside we were always together.

We're not really alike at all, that's the funny part of it. Even back in the fourth grade Tom was a wise guy. He knew everything. Anything he didn't know wasn't worth knowing. He used to call *himself* a wise guy. "You have to be to get ahead," Tom insisted. "You have to take risks and beat the other guy on nerve, by being smart and letting everyone know it."

His father has made it, really big. He's on his way to being top man in an advertising agency. They're local, not a big national firm, but they take in a lot of money, my dad says. Tom's father always has a cigar for people — he even used to give them to us when we were kids. We'd look at the cigar bands, and he'd say, "Why be satisfied with the bands, when you can have the whole cigar?" So we'd go around with cigars, pretending to own ten companies and the bank and anything else we happened to think up. We'd play Monopoly all day, and sit there around the card table, chewing our cigars and drinking ginger ale like it was whiskey. "You three, you're headed for the big time," Tom's father would come in and say. "Which one of you owns the railroads? They're the ones. Everyone says they're dying, but you have to move things, and planes will never do the job the way a long freight does. Look, even in Monopoly there's a railroad on every side of the board, right in the middle. You can't beat them."

Tom's father used to puff smoke right in our faces while we were playing or talking. He'd come in the room and puff a few times on his cigar and joke with us: "How's that for *real* atmosphere!" Then we'd go on, throwing the dice and trying to beat each other out on the property. I always tried to buy Park Place and Boardwalk, and somehow ended up in jail more than anyone else. Tom and Charlie called me "jailbird," the guy who wants to make it real big but slips every time and has to pay for it behind bars.

Once we lit up our cigars. Charlie and I got

sick, but not Tom. Only Tom knew enough not to inhale. His father had shown him. When he went and got the matches — well, I thought he was kidding, bluffing as usual. But he *is* a wise guy, and he really means business. He went ahead, and when Charlie and I hesitated he told us we were chicken and we'd get nowhere. "Now you listen here," he said, mimicking his father. "This country wasn't made big by guys who sit around playing it safe, being scared of their own shadows all the time."

"So," Charlie said, "look who's talking, Daddy." And then we had a big fight. Tom said we'd better put up or shut up, and the game was over so far as he was concerned if we didn't "light up" with him. Charlie said no. It was up to me to do something, one way or the other. That's how it always was — me sitting in the middle in every argument between Tom and Charlie.

That time Tom turned on me, too. He said I had to stop trying to be "nice" and having it "both ways," and finally I got angry at him and said, "OK, let's smoke." Then Tom lit his cigar and passed the box of matches to us. I can still see that box — you know, the red, white, and blue cover with "safety matches" inside, made of wood. Charlie was the one who had the box in his hand, and he just handed it to me without saying a word. I never felt more in the middle. I could feel Tom's eyes on me, and I could see Charlie waiting, just like Tom was. I put the cigar in my mouth and struck the match and put the light to the end of the cigar. Then Tom shouted, "Draw in! You want to *smoke,* not set fire to the cigar." So I did. I sucked on the cigar as if I was trying to get air out of it, and the next thing I knew the cigar was lit, smoke was coming into me, and I was coughing. I felt sick to my stomach, and Tom was laughing, and even Charlie was.

"OK, Charlie, you're so smart, you think it's so funny, why don't you try it!" I said something like that after I was able to talk — and Charlie said yes, he *would,* and he did. He was more careful, but he finally made the same mistake. He drew in too much smoke and swallowed it. Charlie got sick, too, but not as sick as me.

That was the first time we all three smoked, and we were nine or ten. I think nearer ten, because we were in the fifth grade. Tom's father heard about it later that day, and he laughed and laughed, Tom said. His mother didn't think it was all that funny, though. She told us the next day that she hoped we'd never do anything like that again. I thought it was strange that she waited until we were together to say it. Then Tom thought for a second and explained, "It's my dad who decides things. He must have told her it was OK for us to fool around."

After that the three of us had a joke going. We'd come out of the house with cigars, and the other kids thought we were pretty privileged characters. My mother and dad didn't like the idea one bit. They said Tom's father had a real cheap side to him. But they told me one morning during breakfast that they wouldn't interfere. My dad said he didn't want to get any trouble started with Tom's family. He said he wanted *me* to know he disapproved, and he hoped the whole thing was a joke, a "passing joke," he said. My mother agreed, and she added that it was something we were "going through." That's what I used to hear from my mom all the time. "You're going through a stage," or "You'll soon be over this," or "That won't last." What are you supposed to do when they tell you how much they know and make you feel like you're up on a platform performing, and they've read the whole program in advance and know everything you're about to do, no matter how original you think you are? That time I remember my mother saying, "You might as well find out right now that cigars aren't very attractive." When I told her that Tom's father smoked all the time, she said that Tom's father probably did a lot of things that she and my dad didn't like.

My mother and father *are* different from Tom's parents. My father is quiet and always tied up with work. Tom's father is very busy, but somehow he always has time to come by and say something to Tom and his sisters. My father isn't home most of the time. He's a senior partner in his firm, the youngest ever to become one. He always has a "million" things to do, and when I once pinned him down and asked him if he really had that many, he said yes, he did, and life was like that, with too much to do and too little time to do it all.

He's silent most of the time, and from what I

can see, he's very cautious and slow-moving. When my mother and he have a fight, she says he's a "constant bundle of nerves and ideas all wrapped up." She accuses him of ignoring us — there are five of "us," I'm the oldest — and giving all his attention to his work, his "career." And he accuses her of "dragging on him," trying to turn his career into a "social asset." They go back and forth, and end up yelling. It usually starts on a Friday or Saturday when my mother wants to go someplace and he claims there's some "emergency" that has come up. My mother has a lot of friends, and she likes to go out to parties and to see people. My dad, he's a worker — "seven days a week you carry that office around in your head," my mother will say. Some weeks he's *there* seven days, too. The briefs and cases, they just come up, one after another.

"You live pretty good because of him," Tom will say if I criticize my father.

Charlie's father is a doctor, another slave to his work. Charlie and his father have never hit it off, from as far back as I can remember. When we first got to know each other, Charlie would say he might just as well not have a father, for all the time his father spent at home. He's a surgeon, and he's at the hospital every morning at seven o'clock. Charlie says that one thing he knows, he'll never be a doctor. "They help everyone except themselves, and they live shorter lives than other people do." Charlie tells us that over and over. It's really what his father says when he feels overworked.

I used to fight with Charlie over whether his father or mine worked the longest hours and made the most money and would retire first. I think they'll both keep on, though. At least my father will. He says we cost him too much and he *has* to work, to make ends meet and pay the bills for all of us — especially with college coming up for five kids.

I told you I'm the oldest, fourteen, — "a very big, tall fourteen," my mother says. I'm in the ninth grade. Until this year our town had the seventh, eighth, and ninth grades in the old junior high school. This year the ninth grade was moved into the high school.

But all this started long ago. Tom, Charlie,

and I all had tried cigarettes a few times in the seventh grade and more in the eighth. An old teacher once caught us outside, and you would have thought the world was coming to an end, to hear her talk. She said we were only twelve, and at the rate we were going we would be in jail by the time we were sixteen, and we'd die from cancer by twenty-five. She kept on saying she couldn't believe it, she couldn't believe it, she couldn't believe it. We were *children,* still children, barely out of *elementary* school, and *smoking* — smoking as if we had known *how* to smoke for a long time.

Well, as I said, she was right. We tried cigarettes along with cigars a long time ago. They're all over my house, and Charlie's and Tom's. Like with the cigars, it was Tom's idea to start smoking cigarettes, too; only this time he knew his father wouldn't like it, so we did it in secret. Charlie and I were willing, all right. We figured a lot of guys would know how to smoke in junior high.

It's like with drinking. "Things are changing" — that's what you hear people say, my mother and father included. Even when I was a little kid my parents let me drink with them, not a lot but enough to get to my head. I'd get dizzy, and they'd tell me it was good for me to "go through" — then later there'd be no great excitement in my mind about drinking, and it wouldn't be "forbidden," so I'd just take it in stride.

Maybe they were right, because I don't really picture myself being a big-time drinker later on. My dad used to do a lot of drinking, but he has a bad ulcer. He takes those pills instead, but he still sneaks his scotch, mixed with milk. He says that pills can't equal scotch — ever. He envies my mother her "double-blast martini" before dinner. *That* he can't take: "My stomach would disintegrate," he says, "it would just dissolve in the gin and they'd have to do a stomach transplant on me." Then my mother will join in: "If they did, I hope they'd choose the right person's stomach, someone who doesn't want to conquer the world by the time he's fifty years old."

If they're not fighting about anything else, they fight over me or my sister Laura. She's a year behind me, almost thirteen and in the eighth grade. Laura and I are pretty close. She used to imitate me a lot, but now she's off on her own tack — records and a lot of time with her girlfriends talking about clothes and boys. She used to ask me about smoking, and I know she's had wine and sherry and things like that with Mom, but I think she'd be scared of drugs, even if she's curious. Just before this pot thing came up we would sometimes talk and fool around — something like this: "You interested? Would you be if I could get some?"

"Don't be smart, Paul. No one around here can get his hands on drugs. They're illegal, so you have to know a gangster."

"You sure are a kid, Laura. You don't know what's going on. If you have to know a gangster to get drugs, then there are plenty of gangsters all over the place."

"Paul, don't you know that they're dangerous? They can hurt you. I read that marijuana hurts you, and LSD can change your genes somehow. Your children can be born deformed. There's a lot of talk about drugs, but people don't really take them, not people around here, I don't believe."

"Poor Laura, you sound like the little old grandmas who say we're ruining the world, everyone under twenty-one is, because we're so bad and so 'unbehaved,' — that's what one of our teachers said. I don't see why we shouldn't try something if everyone else is, and if it's what *we* want, not what the little old ladies want."

"Where did you get that — 'the little old ladies'? No 'little old ladies' are running anything that I can see."

"Well, I mean old people who don't know anything about what we like — all they want to do is tell us to be like them."

Laura and I can fight, but more than anyone else, even my friends Charlie and Tom, I can level with her. You grow up that close together and you become real friends, even if you do fight some of the time. We go our separate ways but we tell one another things. We can't do much talking with Dad, he's not here. Mom, she has her way of thinking, and we know what it is in advance, so you don't even *have* to talk with her. But with Laura, I can really say it like I feel. She's got her own mind, and she knows that I do, too.

She likes Charlie. She says he's a nice guy — quiet and friendly, and real good to her. She doesn't like Tom as much. She says he's going to get into a lot of trouble before he's through. Sometimes she gets real bossy with the three of us. We'll be around the house and she'll tell us to watch out for the table, or don't break something — things like that. We call her Big Momma, or Momma Laura, and she backtracks — for a few minutes. Then she'll get real cute and want to know if we want something to eat.

"Yeah, Momma, a huge submarine with everything in it, and a tall scotch and soda," Tom will say. She can take him, though, and be real cool.

"OK, Pops. One submarine and a double scotch. Water or soda? Or do you like it on the rocks?"

"Cut it out," is what Charlie or I will say then.

Sometimes, I'll admit, I worry about my three younger brothers. They're only eight, six, and four, but they seem pretty wise to me. They watch us and listen to every word we say. Laura and I feel we're way separated from them — there's five years between her and Ken, who's eight. Laura worries about them more than I do, maybe because she's a girl. She puts it this way: "They're much younger, and they're close together the way we are, but they're around us, too, and they have eyes and ears. Ken may only be eight, but he's a smart little kid, and he's very interested in us. He wants to know what we're doing. We never had an older brother or sister like he does. I think Kenny is really like we were at ten, or even eleven. You don't see it, but he imitates you all the time. He'd rather be with us than with Ricky and Donald. One time he said so. He asked why he couldn't come with us and not be with 'those two babies.' That's what he called them."

So Laura and I talk, and we let each other in on secrets. When this drug scene started getting real, I told her right off, and she made me promise to tell her everything.

"Don't worry, Laura. You can be there if anything ever happens," I said.

"I don't want to be there," she said. "I'm just trying to help."

"I know how to take care of myself."

"You say you do, but I'm not so sure, Paul Larson."

She gets like that at times. She starts calling me Paul Larson and thinks she's talking like a mother. She acts as if she knows everything, as if she could read my mind. She says that I shouldn't hold out on her and I should talk to *her,* not Mom or Dad.

"Dad wouldn't understand, he's too busy. He's got a big case or he's tired, and his stomach is still bad. I heard them talking last night, and the doctor told him to stop smoking and *no alcohol,* even with milk. And Mother, she's worried over that, and if you started talking about *drugs* or something, I think they'd both go wild. A doctor would have to come here with the wagon and take them both off to a padded cell. I don't think you and I realize how hard they both work. All we do is see their bad side. If they make a mistake, we jump on them. Sometimes I wonder why people have kids — they only grow up like you and me, Paul, and make it hard for someone like Dad to breathe. Anyhow, no matter what you say, I think Dad needs rest and quiet and not a lot of misery about you and drugs."

"Don't be so sure," I told her, and I was getting mad. "They read the papers. They're not that out of it. You're so busy building yourself up — Laura knows everything — that you forget about the rest of us. I could talk with them if I wanted. It's just none of their business, and it doesn't have to be yours, either — unless I decide to let it be."

"OK, Paul, I don't want to mess around in your business. I just hope you don't get yourself into a mess of trouble."

I could tell she wasn't really against the whole drug thing. She looked pretty interested. Like always, one minute she'll want to squeal on me for something and the next she'll want to follow right along beside me. Laura was scared I'd get into trouble, but I could see she would go along — if I said she could.

Actually, I was a lot nearer to taking pot than she ever realized — or me, either. I knew all the words — marijuana, pot, grass. And when the other kids talked about "smoking," I knew they didn't mean cigarettes. Then our town paper printed a story on "drugs and youth." It quoted a doctor's talk to the Rotary saying: "Small groups of our high school students are thought to be interested in drugs, and there is considerable discussion of the subject in the junior high school." My father read the article out loud and asked me if it was true. I said yes, that I'd heard about drugs.

"Do you really think it's more than talk — talk by kids?"

"The kids say that in high school they're around, and you can go to parties and get them with no trouble. They say almost everyone in college uses them — I mean pot, that's what they use. Tom's brother — well, he told Tom that he should try it sometime."

"It's a lot of talk, Paul. First of all, you can't get marijuana so easily. It's an illegal substance, and it's a federal crime to possess it and sell it. And anyway, people like to do a lot of talking. They like to exaggerate and spread all sorts of wild stories."

"No." I interrupted him. "Not everyone in school is like that. You don't know. You're not there, Dad. I can tell you, there are plenty of kids who don't make up stories or spread them around, either. They keep hearing things, though, and they can't help wondering what's going on. Tom says his brother has been taking marijuana for two years, ever since he got to college. Do you think Tom's lying?"

"I don't know. Maybe his brother is, or maybe he thinks he has to tell Tom that kind of story. It's a fad, this drug business. It happens all the time — a few people get a fad going, and then others have to go along, or *pretend* they're going along."

"I think Tom's brother has taken marijuana. I'm pretty sure he has."

"How do you know? What evidence do you have? Do you realize that if you *have* any evidence, it's evidence of a *crime?*"

"Well, I've never seen any marijuana, but Tom says *he* has, and I believe him. I can tell when Tom is exaggerating. I know when he makes up a story. He was telling me the truth when he said his brother showed him marijuana."

"OK. Did you ask him when, and where? Did he tell you what happened to his brother when he took it?"

"No. I didn't ask. I couldn't. Tom was too

excited and scared. And Charlie was telling him it was a criminal offense to own marijuana, that the police and the FBI would be after his brother."

"Well, Paul, if Tom was scared, he's smart. The thing for him to do is go tell his parents, so they can get the stuff out of their house."

He looked at me, expecting me to say yes, he was right, but I couldn't even nod my head. I looked at my loafers and sat there waiting for the next question. I just wanted to go away fast.

About a week afterwards Charlie and I were in Tom's house, and I told him what my father had said. Tom got excited and started pacing around while he poured it on.

"Your father, he's a twenty-four-hour lawyer. He thinks he can put the world on the stand and give it the third degree. He thinks everything is the way the lawbooks say. He doesn't know *every-thing*."

"OK, OK," I said, and I really agreed with him. "I know by the way Dad talked that he didn't *want* to know everything, either. Every time I tried to *tell* him something, he jumped at me and tried to tell me what the *law* says, and what the *law* can do, and what the *police* have been accomplishing. I stopped talking with him after a while."

"I know, I know," said Tom. "My father's the same way. He doesn't talk law, he talks about being 'practical.' He says if we don't watch out, my brother and I, we'll get into trouble, and then no business will hire us because we've got a record. He says we should watch out. That's his slogan — watch out, don't get caught. When I tell him that hundreds and hundreds of kids are using pot, he says he doesn't care, he just doesn't want me to get into trouble. And you can't even get him to talk with my brother. He calls him a 'lousy hippie,' just because he lets his hair grow and doesn't wear a tie. I think my brother told my mother about pot and then she told Dad. They didn't say a word to me about it, but the maid heard them talking and told me that my father was real mad and said he hopes Pete gets caught because it'll serve him right. That's what goes on in our house."

Charlie looked embarrassed and said he thought we should stay away from drugs, even if we could get some. Tom got madder and said, "We aren't trying to take drugs. We were just trying to talk to our parents about the thing, and running into a lot of flak all the way. They want to do the talking, they don't want to listen."

"I don't pity you guys one bit," Charlie said. "My father isn't around enough to talk about drugs or anything else. He's too busy prescribing them to others, so why should he talk with me about them? I heard him tell a patient over the phone that marijuana and LSD won't work with terminal cancer. They're not pain-killers, he said. So afterwards, I went up and told him that maybe they don't kill pain, but they might make someone forget his pain, or become more philosophical, sort of.

" 'What do you mean, philosophical?' was what he shot at me.

" 'I don't know — maybe just enough high not to care,' I answered him.

" 'Cancer pain is impossible to ignore. It can be the most awful pain known to man. Drugs like LSD and marijuana aren't what's needed. Pain-killers are needed, and sometimes we even have to sever nerves to make the patient's last days bearable.'

"Now how can I say anything after that kind of speech?" Charlie asked. "I just wanted to leave the room right away. Dad gave me a sharp look, as though he was afraid I might be up to something wrong, but he didn't have the time to find out what. I know what those looks mean: 'I'm busy, Charlie, but you make sure you don't get into trouble.' "

I told Charlie he was right, his father probably was too busy. And so is my father. Then Tom said that the whole point of pot was to slow down people like our fathers, to get them to stop and see something more important than themselves. He went on and on, shouting, "Our parents, they're all locked in. That's their big hang-up — they think they know everything there is to know. My father thinks he can sell the world, and yours thinks he knows every law there is, and yours, Charlie, well, he only knows about sick people. What about a guy who feels good, and he only wants to feel better, that's all, feel as though he's on top of the world, not chasing it around in some office or in a courthouse?"

"You're wrong, Tom!" Charlie shouted back, and I expected him to go on, but he didn't. He paced around Tom's room, saying nothing.

"Prove it," Tom shot back after waiting for a few seconds.

"Prove what? Prove, prove — you're just like my father. He wants proof, and Paul's father wants proof. I'm not against drugs because I agree with *them*. I don't want to cut off my nose to spite my face, that's all. I'm sick and tired of hearing my mother and father preach at me about how good everything *used* to be, and how bad things are now. Who made things bad — us? We haven't had a chance to do anything, yet. But that doesn't mean we have to go kill ourselves just to show a lot of older people how wrong they are. Marijuana is probably dangerous. It's illegal, too, and I'm not going to jail just to feel a little better. I'd rather learn how to drink."

We kept on going around and around. Every few days or so the subject came up. Tom would call us "chicken," and Charlie would call Tom a "bigmouth," and I was in the middle. But more and more Charlie and I began to think Tom was making some good points. He always was a good talker anyway, and he seemed to be fighting for our right to make our own mistakes and see things the way we want to. At least that's how I look at it now when I remember us arguing.

One night — it was a Friday — we were supposed to go to a basketball game and then spin some records at a girl's house, one of Tom's twenty-five girlfriends. (I only have one girlfriend at a time!) We were all three of us to meet at Charlie's house and then walk over and meet our girls. We got to Charlie's and found him mad, so mad we thought he was really going to explode. He didn't say anything. He just glared at us when he answered the doorbell, and pointed upstairs. So we all went up to his room.

"I hate this lousy house. I wish I could walk out of here and never come back."

I was uneasy. I was afraid someone would hear us if we said anything. Charlie saw me move to close his door and said to stop, because only the baby-sitter was around, and then he exploded. "My parents are the biggest phonies who ever lived. They put on a big front for everyone else, but I know what really goes on here. My father will talk to everyone, really sweet and gentle, but *we* pay for it. He shouts at us for nothing, and if we try to talk with him, he turns silent on us. Even my mother gets the cold treatment, but she's learned to dish it out, too. They go day after day, not talking to anyone, including themselves, unless there are people around. Then they're full of sugar and smiles. But as soon as they're alone again, it starts all over. And me and my sister and brother — we're not 'company.' In front of us they glare and look mad — at each other and at us, too. Sometimes my kid sister starts crying at the table. She can't take it, their faces and the silence. Well, tonight at supper I blew up. I screamed and said they shouldn't have had us if that's the way they're going to behave. I shoved my chair away and started leaving the room, when my father came running at me and pulled me back. He didn't even say a word. He just wanted me back there, like a puppet, like one of his patients, staring at him and believing he's God Almighty, who can do no wrong — never ever. Well, I was ready for it. I was ready for anything then. I waited for him to get back to his seat, and then I got up again. I didn't say a word. I just walked out of the room."

Charlie was circling his chair while he talked. We realized he wasn't going to stop, not to go to a basketball game.

Tom said we should get out of the house and go downtown to the drugstore, where we could sit and talk by ourselves. "How can you want to stay here anyway, after what you just said? I feel the way you do plenty of times, but I leave home before there's a scene. I make myself scarce as quick as I can. Who wants to hear all that stuff, listening to them tear people down and praise themselves? My brother is the only one in my family I care about."

For the first time I felt myself a little like Charlie usually is — left out. It was suddenly as if he and Tom had come around to agreeing, and now I was somehow the wrong guy. To make it worse, I found myself defending our families. I just blurted out, "They're only parents, no better than a lot and no worse either. I'm down on mine, too, but they're in a rat race, and they don't know how to get out of it. The best thing to do is forget it. It's not worth it. You can't change them. I've looked at some old pictures of my dad. In high school he was a joker. They voted him 'third funniest guy in the class.' Once he told me he wanted to be a pilot when he went to college. He said he almost didn't even go to college. Then he got trapped, and that's it. The thing to do is not make their mistake. When my dad asks me what I'm going to do, I say I don't know, and I won't know for twenty-five years. They think I'm kidding, but I'm not going to be a slave by the time I'm twenty-one, not if I can help it."

"Cut it," Tom said, glaring at me. He turned to Charlie, who was still pacing around, and said, "You want to go out?"

Charlie paced another time around the room and said yes. I began to feel they wanted me to leave, but I decided to stick with them. I figured

I'd better keep my mouth shut. It wasn't the right time to give a sermon on Be Kind to Parents.

We left and walked downtown. We didn't say a word. Charlie would pick up stones and throw them, one after another. Sometimes he threw one into the street, and a few times he hit a car window or a lamppost. They were really pebbles, and he knew it. He didn't pick up any rocks. As we were walking I saw a few real good-size ones that would have smashed any window in sight. Charlie avoided them, and for a second I felt like picking one up and hurling it right at the window of a car parked nearby. I thought it would be a good way of telling both of them, Charlie and Tom, to stop bluffing. But I just walked along, picking leaves from shrubs and dropping them.

When we got to the drugstore, the jukebox was going strong. Tom and Charlie both ordered coffee, black. I ordered a milk shake. They ignored a couple of kids who said hello. I smiled at the kids. I saw a girl I used to like a lot. She and I had some stupid fight over nothing about a year ago, but suddenly I wanted to go over and talk with her.

But we sat there, still not saying much except a wisecrack here and there at someone we knew. And I decided to stay where I was.

"What a life, working behind a counter. Look at that poor woman. She looks as if she belongs on a hospital ward, getting a long rest, and instead she's smiling at all those jerks and serving them whatever they want. Some people don't know how to get a half-good deal for themselves."

That was Tom, cynical Tom, Tom the wise guy. Charlie just sat there, smiling stupidly at Tom's cracks. I was fed up. We were wasting a good evening. And what about the girls? They'd be waiting for us. I could not sit there another minute. I jumped up and said, "Come on, you guys, let's clear out of here and go someplace. Let's meet the girls and go to the game. Let's do *something*. You want to go home, Tom, or to my place? There's no point sitting here and giving everyone a hard time. That lady behind the counter has it bad enough without us running her into the ground."

Tom said very quietly, "Go home and do your homework."

Then I knew there was going to be a fight if I

didn't think fast. Charlie wasn't saying much of anything, and I couldn't even figure out what he was thinking. I decided to play it as cool as I could, and see where it would get us if we fooled around instead of glaring back and forth.

"Well, I *have* got a lot of homework. I want to be the school's number one grind, and it takes a lot of work. And if I can win over two more teachers, I'll be the biggest cop-out, the biggest teacher's pet in the whole school."

"You're giving yourself away with your jokes, Paul. We know you want to be up top, and so do the teachers." Tom at least half smiled when he said that, but Charlie's face wouldn't crack an eighth of an inch. I decided to keep going.

"Well, Tom, I heard a couple of teachers talking about you, too. They said, 'Watch out for that Tom. He's a real comer. He's slow, but he's going to show his cards one day.' "

Then Charlie stopped everything. "What's the matter with you two? You're babies. We made better sense when we were fifth graders than we do now. Let's get out of here and go home. I'm tired."

We left quickly, just in time to watch the last suburban train stop, let out a few tired passengers, and move on. I saw a newspaper lying on the ground, and picked it up and threw it in a basket. Tom wouldn't let that go by. "Good old Paul. He obeys every law and helps out where other people have fallen down. If he picks up enough newspapers he'll be police chief one day — and then he'll really crack down on people who don't throw their trash in the right place."

I said nothing, and we continued toward our homes. I saw a phone booth up ahead, and when we came to it I went right in. I was going to call my girlfriend and let her know we were not going to show up.

It was a sweaty phone call, and I made it fast. I told her I'd explain later, but that Charlie was sick. When I came out on the street the two of them were still being wise guys. Tom saw the lights go out in a house, and made another crack: "It's eight-thirty, and they're going to bed. This is the biggest bore of a town that ever was. It's dead here, plain dead."

"Why don't you do something about it?" I said

furiously. "You're pretty big on talk, but you're not exactly jazzing things up."

He glared back at me and then he half smiled. "OK, Paul, let's go to my house and I'll show you something."

"What?"

"You'll see."

"Stop faking. If you have something on your mind, let's hear it. Don't waste our time with your mysterious promises that turn out to be nothing but words." I spoke really cool, but I was suddenly scared. I felt like my stomach was being squeezed, and I was afraid of Tom.

"I'm not *promising* you anything," Tom said. "I just said that if you and Charlie come over to my house, I'll show you something. Now that's no big-deal announcement. That's not coming on strong. That's just a simple, low-key statement I made. No one is giving you the hard sell. Take your choice. You can be in bed by nine. Or you can call that nice sweet girl of yours back again and tell her you want to get a milk shake after all."

"OK, you two, stop. Stop. Just stop," yelled Charlie. He sounded almost like he was crying or something. We kept on walking and I clamped my mouth shut hard.

We just walked up to Tom's house and went inside and upstairs to his room. Charlie and I sat down on the bed, not looking at each other, and Tom went right to his bureau. He opened up the middle drawer and started taking out some shirts. Then he put all the shirts back except for one, a blue one. He took the plastic wrapping off the shirt and put his hand inside it, and then he pulled out a little package. It was tissue paper, the kind we used to trace maps and pictures with. The paper was folded up into a neat little square, about three or four inches all around, I'd say, and tied together by string.

Tom put the package on his desk. He looked at me, and half smiled. I acted bored. I got up and walked over to his map, pasted on the wall. I studied Africa and Asia, and waited. Charlie sat there, half staring into space and half watching Tom. He looked as if he was almost asleep.

"What you looking at, Paul?" I suddenly heard Tom ask.

"Nothing."

"Any particular country there interest you?"

"Yeah — China. It's nice and big, and it's got a lot of people. Look at all that land."

"This stuff I've got here in the package might come from China, for all I know."

I turned from the map and looked at the package and then at him. He was watching me, watching me real close.

Finally I gave in and spoke. "OK, OK. What's in it? What have you got there?"

"What do you think?"

Then Charlie got mad. He took off against Tom, speaking real slow and shaky. "Come on. Put up or shut up. You're no big shot. It's getting late, and I'm tired. So open the package and get it over with."

Tom was not bothered, and that was the first giveaway that he wasn't faking. He was as cool as I'd ever seen him, and he began to laugh at us. "Oh, they think I'm putting them on. They don't trust old Tom. Well, here you are boys, have some!"

He pulled the string, and the knot went. He didn't throw the string aside. He kept it in his hand, as if it was precious. He didn't really unwrap the package, he just opened it, and held the paper very carefully. From across the room I still thought it was a bluff, because there didn't seem to be anything in the paper. I thought his next move would be to tell us we were blind, because we couldn't see what he could see.

Charlie just sat there, looking bored and half asleep.

"Well, you two, what's the matter?" Tom's voice was very loud. "Don't you want to come and see? Do I have to do *everything* for you, like bring it on a silver platter?"

He moved toward us, and the next thing I knew he was holding the paper right in front of my face. I could see something now. He had both palms up, and his thumbs were pinching the tracing paper. I saw some powder, green powder, and I thought it was a kind of gunpowder — so help me, that was my first thought. Then I thought he had one of those spices, maybe one I'd never heard of. Tom could see I didn't know what it was, and he didn't want to wait any longer.

"Come on, Charlie, you look, too. You're the one who needs this stuff more than Paul does."

As Charlie got up to come over I began to

realize what Tom was up to. I broke out in a sweat, and I remember thinking, "He's got some kind of drug there, that's what it is, a drug." Charlie looked and reacted like I did — half puzzled and half curious. He didn't say anything, and I didn't either. I could tell Tom wanted us to ask him more questions, that he wanted to shock us. I decided to beat him to the punch.

"So, you got some drug stuff. Very smart of you. Let's all taste it right now. Maybe we could fry up some eggs and sprinkle the powder on them. Drugged eggs, that would be great just before going to bed. My father always says that he's never figured out the perfect bedtime snack. Well, we can let him try this one. It'll look good, too. The green powder on the yellow and white eggs. I like that combination." I hated myself for babbling. I was almost giggling.

"Keep on talking, Paul," said Tom, and his face was very red. "You're showing what a hick you are. I wish I had my dad's tape recorder here, so you could hear yourself yammering."

"What *is* it?" Charlie interrupted. "How are we supposed to know what you've got? For all I know it's oregano, or one of those spices. I used to know them all, and this looks like one or two of them mixed together."

Tom didn't answer. He smiled a bit as he walked over to his desk and carefully put the package down. He folded up the paper a little, so that the powder wasn't completely exposed to the air.

"Maybe it isn't a drug," I thought. "Maybe it's something else, some trick thing that his father brought home from one of his trips. Maybe this isn't happening, and we're not here."

After he put the package down Tom opened the bottom drawer of his desk and started taking things out, one after the other, slowly, until I thought I was going out of my skin. Finally he found what he was after — a pipe, a corncob pipe. He put it next to the package, and then methodically put everything else back into the drawers, in a kind of carefully arranged mess. Then he started talking, almost to himself.

"O.K. We're ready for action. All we need is one pipe for the three of us. I've got the aluminum foil, too — it's under the mattress. Do you want to go on with this, or are the two of you as chicken as I think you are? It's up to you. And if you decide to go along, and if anything happens, don't start bellyaching that Tom was to blame, and Tom got the stuff, and Tom forced you to take it. Tom has it, and Tom will share it, but Tom doesn't want Paul and Charlie bringing the whole town down on his neck."

Charlie and I sat there. I could hear our breathing. I tried to say something but couldn't find a word. Neither could Charlie. He wasn't looking tired anymore, but he seemed lost, trying to figure out exactly what Paul *had,* and what he *meant,* and what he was going to *do,* and wanted *us* to do — and what we *would* do.

It felt like an hour went by, but it was probably a couple of minutes. I thought we were getting into one of those "silence matches" like my mother and father have, where you keep on holding out to get the other guy to talk first, to say anything and break the ice. Tom didn't help. He paid no attention to us as he walked over to his bed and lifted up the mattress and pulled out the aluminum foil. It was just that, a very small piece of foil. He picked up the corncob pipe and started fitting the foil into it. It seems real strange now, as I think back, but at that moment I had absolutely no idea what he was doing. To tell the truth, I thought poor Tom was going loony. I think Charlie thought the same thing. I think he was wishing, as I did, that we could somehow get out of Tom's room and his house. As I say, considering all I know now, all I've gone through since, it's hard to believe how innocent we both were, or ignorant, or something.

All of a sudden Tom broke it up. "You don't know what gives. Well, now's your moment. This here stuff is pot, boys, real pot — grass, good strong pure grass, Acapulco Gold, my brother says. I'm still not registering? You're fighting me. Yes, you are. You don't get me. In Hicksville it's called marijuana — by the squares who don't want it. They have laws, lots of them, to make sure no one gets started. Because if they did let people use drugs, all the phonies and fakes around would be seen for what they are, and people would say, 'No dice, boys, no dice, we want out.' "

He went on, louder and louder, and Charlie's mouth was open. We'd never heard Tom talk like that — not even at his wildest. It was then that I first began to feel like I was on drugs — before I ever touched the stuff. It was listening to him. I mean, hearing his words and seeing him get all excited and angry.

Charlie sat there like me, just staring at Tom and listening. He spoke first. "OK, Tom, OK. So everyone is a fake. Does that include us, and all our parents, and the whole town? What do you want us to do? Tell me, should we go out and confess our sins? Should we all meet in front of the town hall and swear we'll be different?" I wished he'd shut up, and yet I wanted him to keep talking, and I almost loved him right then.

"Look, Charlie, I don't mean you guys, you and Paul, any more than anyone else." Tom spoke more softly, like he was talking to a kid brother. "It's just that here's some good stuff, and I've tried it with my brother, and he uses it a lot with his friends. It's harmless, the stuff is harmless, but the police try to track you down. They don't want you to *see* things, really see them. That's the only conclusion you can come to."

He was quieting down, and what he said was finally beginning to settle into Charlie's head and mine. There's just so much you can take into your mind, and my limit then was lower than it is now. I felt myself wanting to say something, even trying to say something, but nothing came out. For the first time that evening, I really admired Tom. He wasn't doing what we thought — fooling around. He was for real, the genuine thing. I knew he was leveling with us, inviting us to try it, if we wanted. But he wasn't pushing it.

That's probably why we both said we wanted to try the stuff — sometime, but not then. He really seemed to care about that green powder, and the aluminum foil and the pipe, and what it all meant. Charlie and I had never heard Tom put himself on the line about anything, not like he did then.

"I'll tell you how it works. You don't have to try it, or ever even look at the stuff again, but I'll tell you about it. You smoke it, sometimes in cigarettes, but not around here. It's a waste to burn the good stuff in paper. The way I was taught was this way. You get a pipe and line it with aluminum foil. You see those pinpoint holes in the foil? They allow you to draw in on the pipe. You make those holes with a pin. You fill up the pipe just like any other pipe, as if it's tobacco — and then you're ready to light it. The reason for the foil is to conserve the grass and keep it together and not let it spill out or get sucked into your mouth when you inhale. It's much thinner and finer than pipe tobacco — see? — more like dust."

We watched as he went through all the motions of starting to smoke. Then he looked up at both of us. "You have to know how. It's not like smoking a pipeful of tobacco. You have to learn how to inhale real deep, and hold your breath — hold it until you think your lungs will burst. That way you get all the smoke right into the lungs and the blood. Soon it's up to your head, in a minute or two if you really know what you're doing. It's good exercise — you learn how to breathe real deep, and you develop your chest muscles."

I wanted him to go ahead and try the thing, and at the same time I was afraid he would. I kept wondering what would happen to him, how he'd act, what he'd do "under the influence." I thought to myself that he *already* was a different Tom, so far as Charlie and I knew him, and I figured that with marijuana he might really flip. Would he talk differently, get even angrier, start getting foolish and sloppy and stumble all over, the way my parents do when they've had too many drinks?

While I was thinking and wondering, Tom was going through the reverse of what we had watched. He took the pot out of the pipe, and he was so careful it took a few minutes. He told us the stuff was very expensive, but said he wouldn't tell us about that angle, and how he got it, unless we decided to join him and try the stuff. He wrapped his Acapulco Gold up in the tissue paper and tied it all together with the string, and then he put it and the pipe back in his desk, and the aluminum foil back under the mattress. For a few seconds we sat there, not saying anything. Then Tom came up with about the one-hundredth new word I'd heard that evening.

"OK. *Basta.* We're through."

Charlie beat me to the punch. "What's 'basta' mean?"

"I don't know what a language teacher would say, but my brother uses it when he means — like, 'enough is enough,' or 'that's it.' It's just a way of saying we've been on that track long enough, and let's not get stuck there."

"Tom . . ." I started to say something, but suddenly my mind went blank. I couldn't find a word, not one, for the life of me. But it didn't seem to matter, because Tom was different now, much easier to be with than he was earlier. It was like we'd gone through something, just because of what he'd shown us.

"Don't worry, Paul. Stay loose and don't try to sweat it. If you ever smoke pot, you'll realize how much is waiting for you inside your brain. Don't get me wrong. I haven't been taking the stuff that long myself — only a couple of months. But I'm not scared of it now the way I used to be."

That got both Charlie and me going, because
he wasn't trying to impress us any longer, or lord
it over us with all he knew and we didn't. Now I
did have something to say.

"Were you scared at first? How much? Who
was with you? I mean, who gave it to you? Your
brother? Did it take a long time to get used to it?"
I was full of questions, and then I realized I was
running off at the mouth with them, one after
the other. So I stopped myself and waited.

Tom was ready for me. "OK, Paul, so you
want to know. I'll level with you the best I can.

"It was like this. My brother had the stuff, and
he gave it to me. I mean he'd been taking the
stuff and telling me how great it was, and then I
asked him if I couldn't give it a try. He wasn't
sure I should. He said I was too young. So I said
he was eighteen, which was only four years older
than me, and what difference would the four
years make, and he didn't have a very good
answer. Anyway, it took a few weeks for my
brother to come across and agree, and when he
did — well, then I chickened out. Boy, did I. He
didn't push me. He said that pot would be

around for a long time, and whenever I wanted it I could have it — all I had to do was ask. Then I asked him the same kinds of questions that you asked me, and he told me what I'm telling you, that yes, he was once scared, but now he found pot great, really great. And without my asking, he described how his roommate had gotten some, and offered it to him and some others, and how it took a while for him to get started."

Charlie interrupted him. "Tom, you make it sound as if a guy is first scared, then he takes the stuff, then he's happy for the rest of his life, like he never was before. Then he goes easy with the next guy, and introduces him to pot. It sounds like a real nice special fraternity, with no hazing and with nothing that ever goes wrong."

"Look, Charlie, 'fraternity' is not the word. There's nothing so rare or special about pot. Millions of people take it all the time. That's the trouble with us — and I include myself. We just don't know what's going on. All we know is your family and my family and school. No one is leveling with you, I mean like your mother and father. They whisper and keep their secrets — I know, because they do here, my parents do. They don't tell you how much they really drink or smoke, or how many dollars they owe around town. For all you know everything is perfect at home, except when there's a sudden fight, and even then they don't tell you why they're *really* fighting."

"Well, how do *you* know — that there are millions taking marijuana?"

I was glad Charlie put that question to him, because Tom was running away with himself. He was building the whole marijuana thing into a lot more than it is — much, much more. Suddenly I wanted to go home. I felt funny inside. I can't describe it. I had this urge to walk right out of the house and get home as fast as possible, to talk with my parents. I wanted to hear what they thought, only I wished I could talk with them the way Tom had with us, so that they would really have to stop and think and answer me very carefully. Anyhow, before I spoke up or made a move, Charlie did. He completely floored me. He said he'd be willing to try the stuff.

"Look, Tom, it's getting late and we'd better

continue this some other time. I think you're caught in this business, and I'm not sure if we should believe everything you say. But I'm willing to give marijuana a try. I'm not afraid of it, not nearly as afraid as you think. I read the papers and I hear it talked about — a lot of people are supposed to be taking drugs, and they're not going nuts because they do. I don't believe that *millions* of people are on drugs, not by a long shot. Oh yes, maybe if you add China and India and places where they've always used drugs. If you want to set the time I'll come here ready for the action."

I went along with Charlie. I kept my voice very quiet and tried to agree with him completely, even though it scared me, the idea of really trying it. "Me, too. I don't mind trying something. Why not see what happens? It might be good."

Then Charlie started moving toward the door, and so did I. In a few seconds we were both out on the street, walking home together — and away from Tom, thank God. That's how I felt then.

The funny thing was that now Charlie and I didn't have that much to say to each other. I expected us both to go over the whole thing, but we just moved along, every once in a while mumbling something about how strange the evening had been, or how little it turned out we had really known about Tom until tonight. We came to my house first, and I said, "So long," and was starting up the driveway when I heard myself asking Charlie, "You going to tell your parents?"

"I don't know. I don't really know. Are you?"

"Oh, cripes, I don't know, either." I kicked a stone marker in our driveway, then I looked up at the house. I wondered whether they were coming home early or late, and how long I'd have to stay up *if* I did want to talk with them — alone, and away from the others. Then I wondered about Laura and whether I'd tell *her*.

Charlie broke the silence. "My hunch is to keep quiet. What's there to say, anyway? If we start talking, it'll be like squealing, getting Tom in a lot of trouble. In no time our parents would be over at his house, spilling the beans to his parents, exaggerating everything we tell them, and creating a huge uproar. Tom would never talk to us again, and for all we know we might get into real trouble. Bad trouble."

"How do you mean, Charlie? Do you think his

parents would actually go to the police *them-selves,* or to the school people? I can't see them doing that. They're a pretty close family, no matter what Tom said tonight. His father, he's all out for Tom. He'd never get his own son in trouble."

"Well, it's not that simple. Our parents would be breathing down Tom's father's back. A guy like your father, and mine, too, could make Tom's father pretty nervous. He might figure the safest thing he could do, all around, is join up and try to clear *his* name by helping out. The next thing you'd know, we'd hear that Tom and his brother were arrested. I'll bet, I'll bet you any amount, that's how it would happen."

"I'm not so sure." I wished right then that my dad was there, and that we could take him into our confidence, like his clients do, and tell him what we knew and ask his advice. He's a lawyer, he knows — that's what I thought to myself. Then I thought of something else. My father and I can't talk, at least not very well we can't, not now. We used to be close, but we've grown apart. He's busy or away or tired. I've tried to start a talk, and nothing gets going. It's much better to talk with your friends, with people you know, who have the same ideas you do about things. Laura, could I tell her?

All that was rushing through my mind, and Charlie was still walking back and forth in front of our driveway. He must have been having his thoughts, too. I guess we both wanted to sort things out by ourselves, but we also wanted to have each other around.

Finally Charlie said he was going home, and I said I'd see him, and he said he'd see me, and that was that. I went upstairs, and Laura and the other kids were asleep. My parents weren't home, and the baby-sitter had fallen asleep watching television. So I turned off the set and went to bed, and I fell asleep so fast and slept so heavy that the next day seemed like a week later. That whole night seemed a long, long dream.

It had been no dream. I knew that sooner or later I would go through the same thing again unless I dropped Tom. For the next couple of days I kept wanting to talk to somebody. Because Laura's younger and a girl, I thought she wasn't the one I should drag into it. My father, he was the one I should go to see, or maybe my mother and him together. I'd picture myself sitting with him, or with them, but always I'd see them getting very upset and angry, especially if I tried to be fair to Tom. Finally I realized that the only way I could talk with them was to cheat

58 :

at the start. I could tell them Tom was some kind of thief, in serious trouble, and I had found out about it. Every time I imagined my parents' reaction, I was on Tom's side, right down the line. Some of what he said, I'd been thinking for a long time, and I know the same goes for Charlie. Tom had said a lot of the things we felt.

But I knew Tom was putting himself in real danger of getting arrested, and I was afraid that sooner or later I would do the same thing. It was strange — one minute I tried to imagine myself taking marijuana and feeling good and free, the way Tom described, and the next minute, well, then I'd see my father and his friend Judge Mc-Williams standing there shouting me down and telling me I was in real trouble, and with the federal government, not just the town. And I thought to myself that if I didn't smoke, and Charlie and Tom did, I'd end up losing my two best friends.

Anyway, a couple of weeks went by and nothing new happened, except that I noticed two newspaper articles I might not have noticed, about drugs being used a lot in colleges and high schools, too, and about how it wasn't just a very small number who take pot now, not only criminals or kooks, but people like my parents, like me.

Then one night Laura and I were talking about next summer and what we'd like to do, and she said sometimes she felt that she didn't want to do anything, that Mother and Dad were always *doing* things, and she got tired of keeping track of them and their "projects," and tired of trying to follow them. So, I said that yes, I agreed, and like her I didn't know why they did it, keep running that race, that rat race. "For what?" I shouted. "Well, they always say for *us*," was the way I answered my own question. But that's a fake, a real fake, and they know it themselves, just like Laura and I know it.

Laura clapped her hands and cheered, "Great!"

I thought to myself, "She's right with me, right with Tom actually, and so am I." It was safe to tell her, I wanted to tell her. I blurted it all out without giving her a chance to say a thing, and only in the middle did I really realize what I was doing. It must have taken me a long time, half an hour or so, to say all I had to say, and at the end I went to get a glass of milk. I was tired.

When I came back Laura was sitting there, deep in her thoughts. I'll never forget that scene. She was in my chair, my desk chair that swivels, and she had her arms folded into one another, and she was tilted back, with her feet on the bottom part of the chair. She didn't say anything, but I could tell she wasn't excited or afraid, either. She looked me right in the eyes. Then I broke the spell. "Well, what do you think?"

"I don't know, Pauley." (That always gets me when she does that, calls me Pauley. She used to all the time when we were kids, but now it's a special thing, for special times.) "I really don't. My hunch is that you don't, either. I mean, you probably like Tom in a way for daring to be on his own and doing what he thinks is right, but you must worry about what will happen to him — and to you and Charlie, too, if the police find out. It's too bad people can't just leave each other alone. Tom is trying to be different from a lot of people and look into things, and he shouldn't go to jail for that. He's not hurting anyone, not that I can see."

"I agree. The big question, though, is what about Charlie and me, Laura? What do you think we should do? I mean, Tom said he'd be glad to have us try some pot" (I tried to use the word the way Tom does, like any other word), "and what I've been wondering is — well, should we?"

"I don't know, Paul. I don't know what to tell you. In a way I'd like to take some of that marijuana myself. Even in my class I hear kids talk about it. My friend Susan has a brother in college who says he won't try drugs, but he does a lot of talking about it at home. She and I both know that girls a little older than us experiment with it — with pot, I guess. They get it from their boyfriends. They have parties, and they inhale together. You hear them talk about how you feel closer together and the music sounds better if you smoke. I don't believe most of what I hear, though. A few weeks ago Susan asked me again if I'd *ever* try it, a drug. I said, 'It depends,' and she said, 'Depends on what?' and I said, 'It depends on who's taking it and why he wants to take it.' Then Susan brought up the police and the FBI, and how they're trying to find out who's supplying the drugs. Do you know who is?"

"Tom didn't tell us. I'm not sure he knows. I think his brother gets it around college. It couldn't be very hard to get, I know that. Tom says he has enough for plenty of smoking."

Laura wanted to know how you do it, how you smoke, and all that. I was in the middle of telling her when we were called downstairs by Mom. We went faster than usual.

It was a week later that I made my big decision. At least it seemed like the biggest one of my life at the time. Now it's almost funny, thinking about it, because even though it was only a few months ago, I feel that more time than that has passed, like five years, I mean. One thing I know, though: as long as I live I'll never forget the time of the day and the place — Tom's room again, and yes, again it was on a Friday night, and seven forty-five almost exactly, because I remember looking at his desk clock.

It began when Tom called Charlie and me and

asked if we wanted to see a movie. We said sure, and we agreed to meet at his house. It wasn't the first time I'd been back to Tom's house since that evening when he showed us pot. We'd been over there twice, and it was a little embarrassing at first, but no one had said anything. It was almost as though we'd forgotten all about it.

We were on our way to the movies when Charlie remembered he had forgotten his wallet. Tom and I didn't have enough money for a third ticket. There was a pretty good movie on TV for nothing, so we turned around and went back to Tom's.

It was me, I'll admit, who brought up the subject of pot. I said we didn't have to watch TV, either. (I had seen the movie, but I didn't want to say so.) I said we could always entertain *ourselves.*

Tom got a big kick out of that. "Hey, Paul, I think you're going someplace, I really do." He was back on his hippie talk for the first time since we had that night of it a few weeks earlier. It's funny, how he can turn those words on and off. "Yeah, and you, Charlie, are you digging, too?"

Charlie nodded yes. Then Tom turned real serious. "Look, let's not waste time. Let's either get going or not. We either take a trip or we stay home, boys. That's it. You want to travel or not? If you want to try a smoke, I'll get us on the road. If not, let's make the best of a dull evening and see that movie on TV."

This time Charlie took the lead. In fact, he decided things. Like me, he could see that we couldn't have any more long discussions — Tom wanted a yes or no from us. He seemed impatient, in a hurry, and ready to get angry if we didn't either join him or drop the whole business once and for all.

"OK, Tom, Paul and I want to try a smoke. Right, Paul?"

I said yes — fast, before I had a chance to think about it. And Tom was on his way to his desk drawer.

Charlie and I sat there watching, without saying a word. In fact, the room was so quiet it was almost like in a movie. You know — when someone is going through a house at night and trying to sneak downstairs or something, and the whole movie house is suddenly so quiet that you notice it, how quiet it gets.

Then, in a minute, or two, Tom was ready, and he broke the spell. "Let's go now. It's very simple. All you do is draw in and hold the smoke inside you as long as you can. I told you before, but there's no way to learn but to practice, to *do* it. I can tell you right away that this is much easier and much more pleasant than smoking tobacco. Let me begin, and afterwards I'll pass the pipe to you, whichever one of you wants to be next.

"This is how it is," he said. He kept saying that the whole time, and I felt funny hearing him, because it's what he used to say a long time ago when we'd be arguing over something and he wanted to have his say. He'd come out with "This is how it is," and you'd know you were going to hear something straight.

Tom lit up and started drawing in, and stood there holding his breath, and then let it out. He said "Ah" a couple of times after he'd inhaled. In a minute or two he said, "I'm on my way," and then he asked the question I knew was coming:

"Who wants it next?" I answered "Me" so fast and loud that Charlie turned and looked at me, as if to ask whether I was all right. I guess he could detect how nervous I was from that one word "me" — though it was only when he looked at me that I actually realized I might be nervous.

Tom gave me the pipe fast. What I recall most of all now is that for the next few minutes I was *totally concentrated* on *smoking*, on holding the pipe in both of my hands, and drawing the smoke in, and keeping it in, and letting it go, breathing it out. I stared with all my might at the pipe, and before I could wonder how pot would *affect* me, well, I was ready to start again with another drag of smoke.

I must have done like that for a minute or two, I don't exactly know, of course. All I remember is that after I took one of those big breaths, my head seemed to hurt. It wasn't quite a headache, just a kind of swelling of the head as if it had some pressure inside it and was getting ready to take off, go up into the sky someplace like a balloon.

About that point Tom said I should stop for

a while and "let the pot soak into you." I turned and gave the pipe to Charlie, and I knew something was happening, but I didn't know what. It was just that I felt a little fuzzy — that's the only word I can use — and Charlie, he seemed further away from me than he was. What I mean is that as I walked toward him I was conscious of the fact that I was doing it, walking, and also it felt as if I was *on a walk* — you know, a hike or a trip — rather than just taking a few steps across the room. And when I handed the pipe over to Charlie, I watched it and watched his hands take hold of it. I felt as though everything was becoming a little slower.

We went around again, the three of us smoking from the pipe, and after what must have been ten minutes or so, I was right in the middle of some "reaction," as they call it, the doctors and people you read about in the paper. All I knew was that Tom had said that the first time he took pot, nothing much happened, except his heart speeded up and he could feel it beating real fast — while with me, much more than that was going on. My heart seemed OK. I felt a little sick to my stomach, but it didn't last long. Most of all, I felt the slowdown I described, and my head was light, and also, more and more, the look of things began to be different.

I don't mean that I "saw things" or anything like that. It's hard to explain, but the way I'd put it is that I'd notice things more — as I mentioned, things like myself walking, or handing the pipe over to Charlie — and I'd look at things in a different way. Like the rug on Tom's floor — I found myself looking at it, looking and looking, and it made me think of some painting, the kind you see in a museum, with the lines and colors *almost* reminding you of something real, but not quite. Or Tom's wall — there were a couple of pictures on it, but I zeroed in on one little corner of one of them. It was a beach scene, some sand and low bushes, dunes, maybe. It almost felt as if I was in the middle of them, walking on the land and looking at a lake, or part of the ocean that worked its way in between the hills of sand. For months and months I'd seen the picture on Tom's wall, but never like that, never as if I was inside it.

I don't want to give the impression that the three of us sat there like weirdos, or dopes, or in a kind of a trance. We didn't move much, even move the way you do when you sit and squirm or change your position; we just kept on talking, but slower, and when we looked at each other we *really* looked. I mean, when I wasn't busy looking at the wood on Tom's desk — you know, the grain and how all the lines go off and disappear and come back — I was staring at Tom's watchband or at Charlie's sweater, which he was pulling off a little, as though he wasn't sure whether he wanted it on or off. Then, all of a sudden, I thought of Nan, my girl. I hadn't talked to her for a couple of days, but for some crazy reason she was talking to me, loud, it seemed, and I could hear her, and I could picture her, too. I just sat there thinking of her, and I felt as if she was right there, real close by. I *knew* she wasn't there, but I felt as if I could touch her if I reached out.

Naturally, we tried to tell each other how we felt. Tom started it by asking us, and even if he hadn't we would have had to let each other know. Even then I noticed Tom was a little different from us, less nervous maybe. He told us several times not to worry or get panicked, but it turned out that we *didn't,* and I honestly believe that someone who wants to smoke grass could never get a better introduction than the one Tom gave us, so we really could enjoy it.

The main thing we all three discovered was that there are differences in reactions. Tom said with him it was most of all a feeling of "release." He said he felt "high," as if something real good was happening, as if at last he could talk the way he wanted, and even more important, feel the way he wanted.

We talked about what was happening in us, as we were sitting there and passing the pipe around — under Tom's directions to go slow, and relax and take a few drags each time, and then relax and enjoy ourselves. I talked about what I was *seeing,* about the rug, the picture, and Tom's desk, and yes, my girlfriend Nan, too. "Have you ever looked at that desk, Tom? The lines in the wood whirl and swirl, and you can see the straight ones, looking like a road, and nearby are all sorts of curved ones — maybe a lake is nearby. I feel as if I could just stare at it all, or trace the grain on a piece of tracing paper, like I used to do with maps."

Then I looked at a branch of a tree outside the window, and the same thing happened. I mean, I really did look at it — the design to the thing, the way the twigs went off at different angles from the larger branches. It all happens in half a minute, maybe, but you sure see a lot you usually don't. It may just be that in my case I like to look at things, anyway.

Now Charlie, it was different with him. He felt dizzy for a while and light-headed, the way I did, only he said he felt he'd been floating one minute but falling down the next. So he decided to sit squarely where he was and not move an inch. He said his stomach felt funny — first he felt almost like throwing up, then hungry, really hungry. He took some gum that Tom had, and said he wanted to eat it, he was so hungry. Then Tom went and got him some candy and a glass of milk, and they disappeared in about two or three seconds, I'd say. Tom had some Life Savers in his pocket and gave them to Charlie, and he gobbled them up. Then we all laughed, Charlie included. "I feel as though someone is inside me trying to eat, eat, eat. I've never been so hungry — and right after supper! And I feel half excited and half sleepy, a crazy combination, that is. It's like trying to fall asleep, or *wanting* to, but being all steamed up about something, but you don't know what."

Charlie said if we didn't watch out he'd just talk and talk and talk, and he began to, but suddenly Tom stopped him — and stopped me from doing my gazing around. Tom looked as if he was going to start crying, and then he did, not too much, but Charlie and I couldn't mistake those tears.

"What's the matter, Tom?" I asked.

"Nothing," he answered quickly. "It always happens when I smoke. My brother, too — he starts with tears. He says if the pot is real clean and strong, it always affects him like that. He cries and he feels good, both at the same time. He also says he sees something he calls 'light,' little flashes like fireflies or something. I've never had that happen, though one of these days *you* might,

Paul, because it looks like you're the one who's hung up on *looking*. According to what I hear, some guys feel themselves hearing more sharply — they notice every little sound, or change in someone's voice. Others like to feel things — wood, steel, the wall, books, anything. They say their skin is really alive, like electricity. Me — I get to feeling very good, and then for no reason at all I want to cry and run and be by myself, and then laugh and laugh."

For a few minutes — I think it was that long — we just sat there, very quiet. I think we all were hitting the peak of things. Tom said we might as well stop inhaling more pot, because he wasn't sure when his parents would come home.

I began to feel tired and sleepy for a few seconds, but suddenly I was full of energy and ready to do anything. The thing I found most scary was the *thinking* — your mind just rushes along from one thing to another. I never thought I had so many thoughts inside my mind. You know how sometimes, when you're going to bed or just getting up, and you're lying in bed — and your mind just wanders along from one idea to the next, and the ideas keep wiping each other out? Well, that's nothing compared to what grass can do. You just feel a whole lot of things pushing at your mind. It's like a touchdown in a football game. All these things are trying to get through to you, to your attention, and when one of them does, and scores, it's only for a second. Then others are there, waiting to score too. After a while you begin to think it *has* to end, because there can't be many more things left for you to think about, but there *are,* there always are, it seems.

I guess the drug was beginning to wear off when I began to feel *really* lousy. My stomach was upset and I wanted to go home and sleep — like my dad says when he's high on his scotch, "sleep it all off." Charlie was still going strong, though. He suddenly got up, leaned over to tie his shoes, and *stayed* there, in that position. I thought he had hurt his back or something.

"Are you OK, Charlie?" He said nothing, and I repeated the question, figuring the drug had affected his hearing. Then Tom said, "Look, he's OK. Don't worry. He's just trying out the position. Just because most of the time we sit or stand or lie down, does it mean that we *always* have to carry ourselves like that? He's just trying to free himself up. That's what my brother does sometimes. He sticks out an arm or bends himself into some position, and then he holds it — for longer than he'd ever be able if it weren't for pot. He says he's proving that he's not tied down to the same old mold. Charlie is doing the same thing."

Charlie didn't say anything. He just kept leaning over, I thought looking at his shoes. Finally he got up, and I asked him how he felt. He smiled a little sheepishly and said, "OK." He didn't look very "free" to me, just tired and maybe a little mixed up. By that time, you can see, I was getting a little mixed up myself, besides being tired. I just wanted to go home, and it annoyed me that Charlie seemed almost kind of silly, like my mother when she's had a couple of martinis and she starts moving things "for fun" in the dining room or in the living room. Also, I couldn't understand why Tom didn't just give up and stop trying to rub in how wonderful pot was, and how it made you feel like a different person. I felt different, all right, mainly sick and ready to go to bed and sleep a long stretch, twelve hours or more.

*A*ctually, one of the funny things about that evening was how I *did* get home and to bed. I don't really remember how. It wasn't that I was drunk, or knocked out, or anything like that. Suddenly I became very tired, so tired that I must have been half asleep walking home. The next day, when I woke up, I kept wondering how I got to where I was, in my bedroom. Charlie told me later that I walked home with him, drowsy and silent, but on my own feet, on my own steam, all the way.

I woke up that morning late, nearly eleven

o'clock. It was Saturday so I could get away with it, but Laura was curious, and so was my mother. Laura kept on giving me looks, and I knew what they meant: "Where *were* you, Paul, and what did you do?" And my mother, she reminded me three times in about five minutes that I *slept late.*

I had a headache most of that next day, I think because I kept on pushing at my brain to remember everything that went on the night before. I must have seemed funny or looked funny because Laura asked me if I was OK, and when I said yes, I was OK, she told me she didn't believe me one bit. Then, late in the afternoon, Charlie called me and said he had slept most of the day and waked up wondering if we'd *really* spent last night the way he thought we did. I kept on telling him not to worry, that all we'd done was take some pot, and Tom had done it many times and seemed in good shape. We talked a long time. Finally I told him to calm down and then call back. Charlie said he'd call in an hour.

When I got off the phone and found Laura nearby, I could tell from her look that she'd been hiding and listening to me.

"OK, Miss Spy, so you have nothing else to do but listen to me talk on the phone."

"What do you mean?"

"What do you mean, 'what do you mean?' You heard every word, didn't you?"

"Paul, I think you're losing your mind. I really do."

"What do you mean?"

"Now who's asking 'what do you mean?' You know what I mean."

"No, I don't. All I know is that I know your face upside down, inside out — I can tell when you're lying, pretending, or anything else. You were hiding around the corner, trying to figure out what Charlie and I were talking about, weren't you?"

"I didn't even know you were talking to Charlie until just now, when you told me. I was in my room until a couple of seconds ago."

"Yeah. I know. Innocent Laura, who always minds her own business."

"Well, I'll tell you, Paul, *someone* had better help you mind *your* business. You look real strange to me, and I could tell from the way you were talking to Charlie that something strange is going on. What are you and Tom up to?"

"Nothing. What's it to you, anyway?"

"Oh, nothing. I don't care. You're only my brother, and I've only known you ever since I can remember. But that doesn't make any difference. If you're in trouble, it's none of my business. I know that."

I don't know why, but she got to me, Laura did. I must have been upset, more than I knew. The next thing I knew, I was pouring it out to her, everything that happened over at Tom's — and she didn't seem in the least surprised or worried. Suddenly I caught myself and *asked* her, "Laura, doesn't this stuff bother you?"

"Well, no, not really. I mean, I'm not happy about it, but that's because you're not, either. You'll get into trouble if you keep on taking drugs, and I guess you're afraid of that, too."

"What kind of trouble?" I knew the answer, but I wanted to hear her say it.

"With the police or a teacher, or with Dad."

"What would the police do?"

"I don't know. But it's against the law. And

you hurt yourself if you take drugs. You do something to your brain and your blood, or something. I just remember that Dad said drugs were bad, and he seemed to know what he was talking about."

"Well, there's a lot of things that Dad *seems* to know about. I'm not sure how much he knows and how much he *says* he knows."

I waited for a few seconds, and then I practically surprised myself with the question I asked Laura: "Would *you* take marijuana — if I got some and took it with you?"

She wasn't exactly knocked over, and I was proud of her. "It depends. I don't think so. I'd want to, but I'd be scared. I might do it, though, if you knew what to do and showed me how and I was sure it would be OK. I hear the girls talk. Some of them have brothers and sisters who use drugs, or boyfriends, or they've tried them themselves. They're all curious. They all want to know *what* happens."

"I'm not sure myself what happens, even though I took the stuff with Tom and Charlie, and saw them take it. To tell the truth, I'm wondering what will happen if we keep on taking it, every week, the way Tom says he does — and I think he's telling the truth. We're supposed to meet next week in his room — again. We're supposed to take it again. That's what has Charlie worried. He's afraid something will happen to us physically — that we'll have an aftereffect, a reaction of some kind. He's thinking of mentioning the subject to his father, to see what he says."

"Maybe he should. Then you guys could at least get the facts straight. I mean he's a doctor, and wouldn't he know if there was anything that might happen? I heard one of the girls say that her brother said some drugs are really dangerous — they don't wear off for weeks or even months."

"That's a lot of crazy talk. I don't believe it. I'm no different now than I was two or three days ago. I went through something unusual, and that's it."

"Well, if that's all, then why *don't* you talk to Charlie's father — or to Mom and Dad?"

"You know why I don't talk with them. Who can talk with Dad? He hasn't got time to talk with himself. *He's* the one who needs to smoke grass, if you ask me. Now he can't drink anymore,

he's worse than ever — busy, busy, busy, and like
Tom says, all hung up about *everything*. If he'd
stop and take a *look* at things — the way you do
with grass — then he might relax and be better to
have around."

"I don't think you see Dad's side of things,
Paul. You really don't. He *has* to work all the
time. What would happen if he lost his job?
We'd never get to college, and we'd lose this
house, and everything. He's not ignoring us, or
forgetting about us. He's working for us. I once
heard him telling Mother that he was real sorry
it was this way, that he didn't see much of her
and especially us."

"Well, Mother isn't any better. What's *her*
excuse? Have you ever seen that calendar she
keeps over her desk? She has something written
on every box, beside every day of the year. She
blames Dad when he's not home for supper, but
she's hardly home in time herself. She dashes off
here and there. She could sit here at home and
smoke pot and feel real good and relaxed, and
she wouldn't have to run around seeing all her
friends and like that."

"Come on, Paul — she just likes to *do* things, that's all. What do you want her to do, sit here all day, if she doesn't like it? I thought you once said people should leave each other alone. Well, why pick on Mom? She's around enough. If you really wanted to talk with her, or with Dad, they'd come running. I know they would. I've heard them say so. I heard them say a few months ago that we should all go off on a trip together, maybe up to Vermont, where we could just loaf around and eat and take hikes, the whole family and no one else."

"I've heard them say that for years. They feel bad for a minute, when they have the time, and then they say we should all be together out in the country someday. You know, we're out in the country *right here*. It takes an hour to get into the city. There's plenty of trees and grass — that's why we live here. So why go up to Vermont? Why don't we go out in our own backyard together?"

"Because we've all got things we have to do, every day. That's why."

"Yeah, that's why. And that's why I think Tom is right: you need something like pot to make you stop and think. I don't want to get hurt because I took a drug, but I don't want to get caught the way Dad is caught. Is that living?"

"You're really mixing things up, Paul. I don't see how all those things go together — Dad and his work and Mom and drugs. Maybe Dad *should* do something else — he says himself he'd like to be a teacher. But why should *you* take drugs because of that? Don't a lot of poor people take drugs, and where do the drugs get them? They end up stealing, to pay for the drugs. I saw that in a television program. A lot of the people lived in awful places, and they were paying money for drugs to inject in their veins, instead of buying food for themselves and their kids to eat."

"Oh, come on, Laura. We're not living in some slum. A lot of cop-outs take drugs. But they're not the same drugs I'm talking about. That's cocaine, or like that. That's the stuff they use in jazz bands, or like that. It's not the same."

"I'll bet the stuff you and Charlie and Tom took, I'll bet the jazz musicians use it, too, and I'll bet they're sorry. They'd just as soon not have drugs with them all the time just to feel good."

"You don't know what you're talking about. Pot doesn't make you into an addict, a drug addict. That's something different."

"How do you know? How do you know it's something different?"

"I just do. Tom told Charlie and me that, and besides I read it someplace."

"Well, you'd better make sure. That's all I have to say. I don't think we know what's going on. Let Tom experiment if he wants, but you should get things clearer. I mean you should find out what the difference is — between all those things, those drugs."

"I know what happened to me. I was there. And so was Charlie."

"Does he agree with you?"

"Yes, I think so. Not exactly, but mostly. From what he said just now on the phone, he agrees, but he wants to tell his father and see what he says. I told him that he was making a mistake. It'll only get his father upset, and he'll come screaming at Tom and me, and Charlie will be kept under lock and key."

"Well, I'll be honest. I'm glad. I hope he tells

his father tonight, and I hope his father comes over here and talks to you."

"OK. OK. That's enough. I'm going out. You just keep quiet. Hear?"

"I promise. It's up to you if you want to get in trouble — well, it's up to you whatever happens. I'm not going to tell anyone anything."

I left. I was getting angrier and angrier at Laura. I felt my legs stretching, a sure sign that I wanted to move. I began to see her as a real fall-guy type — for my parents. But as I look back at it now, I think she got me nervous, even more nervous than I already was, and I think she really was more on my side than either of us could admit. Besides, I had just heard Charlie — telling me he was a "little worried" and he thought it might be a "good idea" to "mention the thing" to his father. I'd asked him *why* he thought it was a good idea, and he really didn't have anything to say, except that his father was a doctor, and he knew things, and he could at least explain it to us — what we took, and why it did what it did to us, and what would happen if we took it a lot, like Tom. I told him that *sounded* good, but it wouldn't happen that way. Instead, we'd all three of us have our parents and the police breathing down our backs so fast it wouldn't even be funny.

Because of my talk with Laura — I think — I called Charlie right back. I thought to myself as I dialed, "It's just Laura. She can get anyone upset."

Anyway, Charlie was like before, wanting me to come over so that I would be there, too, when he cornered his father.

"What makes you think you'll be *able* to see your father? He may be busy or out."

"No. We can. I called his office and asked him if I can talk with him. He was afraid that something was wrong, but I told him no, nothing is wrong, I just want to talk. He probably thinks I'm up to something — but at least he's going to be here, and listen. He said we can talk in his study, private."

"What do you mean, 'we' can talk? Did you tell him that *you're* going to talk with him, or you and *I* are going to?"

"No. I said me . . . I did say you might want to come over, too. And Tom . . ."

"Are you out of your mind? Do you think Tom

and your father could last in the same room for five seconds?"

"Well, probably not. I actually did call Tom. I put it to him straight. I told him I felt nervous, but I didn't know why. I told him I wanted to ask my dad a few questions, and did he want to come over. He laughed so hard I thought he was going to explode. But he didn't — he said, 'OK. Go ahead, and let me know what he says.' "

"He did? Are you sure?"

"Word for word. I think he was half laughing. I don't think he's going to let my father influence him, one way or the other. But I think he was sort of interested — yes, half interested, anyway, in what Dad would tell us."

"What time?"

"Seven-thirty, after Dad has his supper."

I went early, like Charlie suggested. I figured we should talk before we saw his father. I could tell something funny was going on in Charlie's house, because his mother gave me a long look when I came, as if she wondered what I had to do with Charlie's call to his dad. Actually, I've always liked Charlie's mother. She's a real honest, friendly person. A while back I used to think she was the best there is, though Charlie disagrees. He says *my* mother is real good. But his mother smiles more, and she cooks better. When we went up to Charlie's room he said his mother had been real nice. "She asked me five or six times if everything was OK. I said yes, it was, and not to worry. My father must have called her right up. I think they're pretty curious, maybe even worried."

"Well, I think *we* should be worried. What do you think they'll do? I heard over the radio this afternoon that some kids from school were arrested, caught with drugs. I called Tom and he said to stop worrying, that they were fools to be hanging around school with pot. He said a lot of people use the stuff, but they do it in their homes, where no one bothers them. But maybe the kids were turned in by their parents."

Charlie was mad, I could tell. When Tom gets angry, he shouts; with Charlie, it's silence. He glared at me, and finally he spoke: "Look, Paul, relax. Go get some ice cream. We have your favorite in the freezer. Go get some."

"Come on, Charlie. I just don't want us to make any trouble."

"Neither do I. I'd like to try again. That's the way I feel. I mean, to try some more pot. But I'm also going to find out more than we know about the stuff. That's all I want to do. And that's all that will happen — my dad will talk with us and explain things. If he starts jumping on us, well — you'll see, he just won't. He's *my* dad, I know him. He'd never turn us in to anybody, never."

We dropped the subject. Charlie wanted to know how I was "doing," and I said, "fine." He gave me the same kind of look his mother gave me, and I guess for the same reason, because he wanted to know something. I could feel him trying to get up nerve to ask me if I *really* felt "fine." I thought to myself that Tom made a mistake, letting Charlie in on the grass. Charlie is like his father; he worries, and he's always trying to decide if something is "good" for you, or if you're doing the "healthy" thing. So I was feeling trapped, in a way, and annoyed, too. But I also was glad that we'd get a chance to talk with Charlie's father. I'll admit that. I know it now, and I can remember thinking that Charlie's father would at least give us the real lowdown, the medical lowdown, so then we could really enjoy pot, if it turned out he thought it was safe and OK.

Then he came, the same Charlie's dad that I'd known ever since I can remember. He was a few minutes early, and I could see that he was curious, like us. He was pretty smooth, too, and he didn't waste any time, either.

"Well, Charlie — and Paul — what shall we talk about? You name it, and I'll do my best."

"OK, Dad. We might as well tell you what's on our mind, and not beat around the bush. I know you're busy, but I — we, Paul, and me — we have something to tell you, and ask you about."

His father nodded, and looked at Charlie and then at me. He sat still in his chair for a few seconds, then he started pulling his socks up, and then he took out his cigarettes and lit one up. I thought that was very funny, but Charlie didn't seem to be getting the point. I winked at him while his dad puffed out his first mouthful of smoke — and he gave me a blank look in return.

Then Charlie plunged in. He took a deep breath, paused, and came out with his sentences, fast and straight to the point. "Dad, we want to know what you think about marijuana, about drugs like that. We want to know what it does to you, and if it's all right to take it and what you think. The reason is, well, the reason is because Paul here, and me — well, we both have already tried it — only once, at Tom's house just last night. We didn't take much, and we're both feeling fine. There's nothing wrong with us. I promise there isn't. But we were talking, and we thought — well, we thought we'd ask you what doctors think about — about drugs."

His father sat still for longer than either of us expected, Charlie or me. I thought he'd start firing questions at us, pronto. Charlie must have expected some quick action, because I noticed that when he was through with his speech he settled back in his chair, sort of like an army that has opened up with planes and guns, and then digs in and waits for the enemy to answer back. Instead the two of us stared at the doctor, and that was it: he looked like a doctor who was trying to figure us out, his two patients. When he *did* start talking I knew — before he said much of anything — that Charlie was right. I could tell by the man's voice. He wasn't going to get excited because his son, his son Charlie, went and got himself in trouble. Oh, no. He wanted to "clarify" things, that's what he said. That's how he started. And I was glad, and felt safe — but I was also disappointed. I'd have rather seen him *react, react.* Like Tom says, we don't react much, anymore. Everyone wants to be "cool." I think Charlie's dad and mine are alike. I think my father would have done like Charlie's, be cool, speak cool, act cool. Some guys my age say they've learned how to be cool, but I think there's nothing *new* in that.

I saw the doctor pull himself together, take off his glasses and clean them with his handkerchief, stare at us while doing it, and then start in. "I'll be frank with both of you. I'm surprised to hear what you've told me. More than surprised, I'm very concerned. I've read about high school and even junior high school students using drugs — experimenting with them. But I never expected to hear that you, Charlie — or you, Paul — were doing that."

He stopped, and seemed to be asking himself what tack to take next. I expected him to start preaching at us, but he didn't.

"I'm glad you two decided to tell me this. I'm more than glad — I'm honored. If you hadn't I would have been hurt, very hurt. The only thing I can say is that in return I'll try to be as helpful as I possibly can. I know you both have questions about drugs — so do we, the doctors. We don't have all the answers, no one does. But it's good to ask what we *do* know, and if you want me to, well, I'll tell you that."

He didn't seem like Charlie's dad, the man I had seen and known almost all my life. He was sort of remote and professional. At first I found myself disliking him, figuring him to be another fraud, eager for money like Tom says, and a stranger to Charlie, his own son. But he seemed more and more OK as he talked. He was still pretty sure of himself — his manner, I mean — but his voice got to me. I could sense that he was trying to get to us, and I wished Tom was with us. He'd have the answers, he'd tear into the Doc, but I knew this man was trying, and Tom would sense it as I did.

Charlie and I sat there, not knowing even what to *ask*. I guess I wanted to know everything the Doc knew — and that's what he must have figured, because he just started in and talked and talked.

"Maybe all I can do is just tell you what I know, and then we can talk as long as you want. So far as I know marijuana comes from a plant, the hemp plant. What people call pot or grass is the dried-up top of that plant, the leaves and the flower. It's called all sorts of names all over the world, like 'hashish' or 'bhang.' As you probably know, there's nothing new about the use of marijuana. It's been used for thousands of years all over the world, particularly in the Middle East and in Asia. It's not used by doctors here in America. I don't have to remind you, I hope, that it's an illegal substance here; its distribution is forbidden under a federal law. So far as I know, it can be smoked or chewed or sniffed — and I think cigarettes or a pipe are favored in the western world.

"Now, what does it *do?* I'll tell you. It affects what we call the central nervous system, the brain and the spinal cord. In that sense it's like alcohol or sleeping pills or pep pills or pain-killers. They all change the way you feel things, or look at things, or sense things — to different degrees, of course, depending on what you take, and how much. Marijuana acts quickly, as you probably found out. In a few minutes your mind is affected, and it may stay affected for three or four hours. Again, it's like alcohol.

"What happens is that the mind or brain is made both excited and depressed, or toned down or dampened, however you want to put it. Let me explain. Like with alcohol, the part of the mind that broods and worries and concerns itself with problems, or with what is right and wrong, with what is the 'good' thing to do — that part of the mind is somehow released, or made less influential. You've seen how when I take a drink or two I not only relax, but I might say, 'To hell with everything I have to do or ought to do. To hell with it even if it *is* important.'

"Likewise, a person's ordinary reflexes are slowed down by pot, just as by alcohol. You don't react as quickly and smoothly as you ordinarily do. You're less alert and active and coordinated. Of course, you'll say that you're *more* alert —

and you may be, in the sense that the part of your brain that *thinks,* that has ideas and thoughts, is often stimulated by marijuana. In fact, people notice that they are often *flooded* with ideas — they come one after the other, and there seems no end to them. Other things happen, too. Time seems different — a second may seem like a minute, and a minute like an hour. And your sense of distance may change — something near you may seem very far away, or vice versa. A thing across the room may appear right on top of you."

He stopped for a few seconds to catch his breath, and he looked at each of us, right into our eyes. I guess he wanted us to ask questions, but I didn't have any, and Charlie didn't seem to, either. I was fascinated listening to him. He was putting together the whole evening we had — and I knew right then that a lot of people must have gone through exactly what I had, if a doctor could describe it like that. Anyway, he started in again.

"There's not too much more to say, actually. There are other things that happen, and you probably know about them, or may even have experienced them. The effects vary from person to person — that is, some people feel light-headed, or they get dizzy, or they feel they are floating, or they hear ringing noises in their ears. Some people see things — they see things that aren't actually there, or they notice things that are there in a new way. They concentrate on a particular detail of something, or suddenly they feel themselves looking at 'the whole room,' and claim they see it differently.

"I think I should also tell you that many people are affected by *physical* changes as well as psychological or mental ones. They may get sick to their stomach, or feel their heart pounding away. We know that marijuana causes the heart to beat faster, the blood pressure to go up, and more sugar to go into the bloodstream. As a result, often one gets hungry, wants more sugar, more candy or other sweets.

"Frankly, from what I've heard and seen, the reactions to the drug vary with the person who takes it. If someone is moody, feeling low, down and out, he's probably making a mistake if he thinks that marijuana will pick him up, make him feel better. Instead, he may get more anxious, more scared, more upset, and even become panicked. If he's already in good spirits, he may become so confident and 'happy' that he forgets all the ordinary common-sense precautions that go with living, like watching out when you cross the street or drive, or things like that. He may get overly restless, talk a blue streak, laugh at things that aren't really funny, and in a way lose a lot of his connection with other people. In other words, he can become so wrapped up in himself that he doesn't really care what the people around him are thinking or doing — or what they think of him, or even whether they can understand him at all, what he's saying or laughing about, what his jokes mean, and that kind of thing.

"And like any drug that affects the brain, or in fact any drug at all, marijuana can be dangerous and harmful. It can cause a person to become confused and overcome by fear and tension. He can lose contact with the world, and be what you might call 'crazy.' That is, he seems off in another world. He shakes, and hears strange noises and voices. He has visions. He doesn't know where he is, or who he is, or what day of the year it is. He's really 'gone,' or 'out,' is the way you can put it. I'm not saying that it's the *rule,* but I'm saying it *can* and *does* happen.

"Which brings up the question of dosage. You know with the drugs I prescribe, the pharmacist gives the patient exactly what he needs, what I think will do the job — no more and no less. Even with alcohol, you know what you're getting when you buy a bottle of whiskey and start pouring it into a jigger. But it's different with marijuana, and I think you ought to think about this, if nothing else. No one knows *what* he's taking when he uses marijuana. It's an illegal drug, and much of it is distributed by gangsters and racketeers — men who control gambling and engage in all sorts of shakedowns, payoffs, and bribes. They smuggle marijuana from places like Mexico, then distribute it. Of course, ordinary individuals also smuggle it in and distribute it. But no one knows exactly what they're getting, and very often what you get is mixed with other things, to weaken it *or* make it even more powerful. The distributors weaken it to get more mileage out of the marijuana they have, or they mix in LSD or even Dexedrine to make sure you get excited and stirred up and experience the reactions you're supposed to be looking for.

"I'm no drug taker, but I know the term — they say it's 'laced,' the marijuana is *laced* with other things. And if one of them is LSD — well, I can tell you as a physician that you're in *bad danger.*"

"Of what?" I asked. "Of becoming an addict or like that?"

"No. Marijuana and LSD are not addictive drugs. They may cause you to forget about the real everyday world and 'tune in' more and more on yourself and what *you* think and feel, but they're not like heroin, say, which you *have* to take, once you're hooked, if you're to avoid getting sick, with vomiting and pains all over the body. What *is* dangerous about LSD is that it can take effect hours, even days after you've tried it — so that you never quite know when or how it will work — and it even seems to affect your genes, through which we transmit ourselves from one generation to another. In other words, LSD can injure the body and really linger in it — and strike when unexpected."

"What do you mean, *'strike'?"* Charlie asked. He was getting real nervous, and so was I.

"Well, we don't know *how* LSD works. We just know it causes severe reactions in people. They become extremely unhappy, frightened, and sometimes quite wild, hard to understand — and, well, what we call crazy, or insane. That is, they hear things and see things. They can't be easily understood by others, and they themselves can't figure out what is happening to them, in their minds. They often think they can do impossible things — fly, move buildings with a word or a gesture, change the whole world, speak to dead people, and such. They lose interest in *doing* things, in the world outside their own minds. They not only spend an hour or two being 'high' or excited, but they spend weeks and weeks going over a particular idea, or being confused, and confusing to others. Many of them have had to be admitted to psychiatric hospitals and treated there for weeks."

"What's wrong with thinking about some-

thing for a long time, even if you don't do anything about it?" I *had* to ask him that. I felt him
winning us both over without even a fight. He
seemed to know so much, and it sort of bothered
me, the way he just kept on talking, talking, talking. I was getting scared that we might have
taken something like LSD with the pot, or that
Tom would do it one of these days. And I kept
on wishing that Tom was there, to answer him
back.

"I'll tell you, Paul, there's *nothing* wrong with
concentrating on a thought — even for years. It's
just that I don't think the people who do so
under the influence of LSD really succeed in
what they're trying to do. I mean, they don't
really pull their thoughts together, express them
in ways that others — or even they — can understand, and *do* something with their thoughts by
writing them down or expressing them on a can-
vas, or in a piece of sculpture, or *anything*. It's
like a lot of dreaming — they experience one
image after another, and finally become weary
and confused — and some of them, very very dis-
turbed."

Charlie looked pale. His father noticed it, too.

"Are you OK, Charlie?"

"Yes, I am. It's too much for me, all you've said. I mean I don't know what to do with it. I've been sitting here listening to you, and at first I thought you were trying to *persuade* us — and then I began to feel no, that the whole business of taking drugs isn't so simple as Tom says, and that it's dangerous, more than he knows. But I still agree with a lot that he says — that there's a lot of fake things around, and that his father gets drunk and takes pep pills to wake up in the morning and sleeping pills to go to sleep, and that pot is no worse than that, and it may be better, because it gets you thinking about things. So, anyway, I'm just feeling mixed up. That's all."

"Well, Charlie, in a way that's the way I think you *should* feel. I'm *not* defending alcohol, pep pills, or sleeping pills. I'm not trying to say people like me aren't full of faults. I'm not even trying to say that marijuana can't be an exciting or stimulating experience. I know as a doctor that it literally is, that the body and mind *are* jazzed up by the drug.

"All I'm trying to tell you is that when you

talk about drugs or take them you're involved with illegal substances that can be and have been dangerous. In other words, you're breaking a federal law when you obtain and use marijuana, and you're causing mental troubles for yourself *that* way, if no other way. I mean you're putting yourself in danger, risking arrest and jail. Doesn't that do something to your mind — make you afraid, nervous and anxious, and make you feel bad, or in danger? And as I said, like alcohol, marijuana can get you to feel dazed, confused, or dangerously sure of yourself — to the point where you'll do things like speed and get in an auto accident. Yes, it's old hat to say 'Two wrongs don't make a right,' but I think that applies here. And as for LSD, well, I've made my point there. Most students, I notice, are staying away from LSD, even a lot of the hippies. They're right to be scared."

We sat there, saying nothing. Finally Charlie's father was smart enough to say he had to go. He could see that we didn't have anything more to say. We needed a rest from him and his information. He shook my hand and said we could talk with him again anytime we wanted.

When he left, Charlie and I were pretty quiet. We didn't want even to talk to each other. Charlie said he wanted to take a walk by himself and sleep on it, and I agreed. When I got home I went right to my room and did that, went to sleep.

In a way, that's all that has happened. Charlie and I have "slept on it" up to now. I mean, we decided not to smoke any more pot. We talked and talked with Tom about it. In fact, we had some real swinging talks. He even "turned on," while we argued and tried to tell him to lay off for a while. We said people are already mixed up, and pot only makes it worse — and he said we'd been brainwashed.

"You're both chicken is what it all comes down to," he said at the end of our marathon argument.

"We're both sleeping on it for a while," I said.

Tom says that we should "feel everything," and that's the big thing in life. Sometimes I agree, but I guess a guy like Charlie or me needs to do things different from Tom, go slower maybe. He still tells us we should take more "trips" with him, but I tell him I think he can travel his way, and I'll go mine — and right now I don't know which way mine is, *where* I'm headed. Tom says that with pot you "see through" people and you ignore what's unimportant; you sit back and laugh at the world. But I think I'd rather change a lot of things I don't like. You get tired of sitting after a while, and even tired of laughing. You want to go out and *do* something.

Anyway, Laura and I don't talk much anymore about Charlie and Tom and pot and things like that. There's just too much that I have to do, and that I want to do. Tom says that he's doing his "thing" and I'm doing mine, and he's right. The other day he asked me again if I wanted to try more pot, and I said no before I really thought about it. Then he wanted to know if I was against his smoking it, and I said no again, just as fast. It wasn't my "thing." He said he couldn't argue with that — and that's how it is right now.